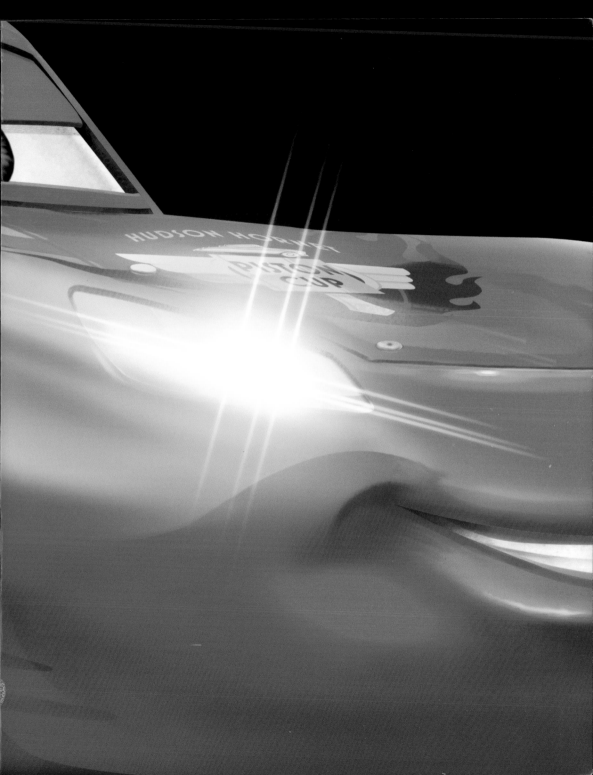

First published by Parragon in 2012
Parragon
Chartist House
15-17 Trim Street
Bath, BA1 1HA, UK
www.parragon.com

Edited by Katrina Hanford
Designed by Joe Scott
Production by Jack Aylward

ISBN 978-1-4454-8707-6

Printed in China

RACE TRACK RIVALS

By Susan Amerikaner

Illustrated by Scott Tilley, Andrew Phillipson, Janelle Bell-Martin,
Dan Gracey, Seung Beom Kim, and the Disney Storybook Artists

Bath • New York • Singapore • Hong Kong • Cologne • Delhi
Melbourne • Amsterdam • Johannesburg • Shenzhen

Lightning McQueen and Francesco Bernoulli had challenged each other to a race in Monza, Italy—Francesco's hometown.

"Benvenuto!" said Francesco. "Your plane was late, but this is no surprise. You will be late crossing the finish line, too."

Lightning smiled. Then he whispered to Mater, "I am so beating him—right here on his own turf!"

As they left the airport, the cars were surrounded by photographers.
"Everyone loves Francesco. He has too many fans," said Francesco.

"Nobody has more fans than Lightning!" Mater piped up.

Francesco rolled his eyes.

"We will prove it!" said Luigi. "Lightning gets hundreds of fan letters each day. Guido, bring the mailbags!"

Guido zoomed off!

Guido returned with mailbags overflowing with fan letters. Lightning was a little embarrassed.

"Oh, it's really not that big of a deal," he said.

"You are right, Lightning," said Francesco. "It is no big deal because Francesco has much, much more fan mail!"

"Letters are great," said Lightning. "But we like to get some
fender-to-fender time with our fans whenever we can."
Lightning and his friends greeted all the cars who were lined up to see them.
Mater really got the fans going. They began chanting: "Light-NING! Light-NING!"

"Questo e' ridicolo!" mumbled Francesco. "And what about autographs?" he asked. "Watch—and be amazed."

Francesco was not impressed.
"Francesco never guzzles," he said.
"Oil should be savored."

Lightning cruised over to Francesco. "How about a warm up before the big race—just you and me?" he asked.

Francesco nodded. "Ah, good idea, Lightning! Try to keep up, if you ...."

Before Francesco could finish, Lightning was a red streak down the road!

"Ka-*ciao*, Francesco!" yelled Lightning.

Francesco was just about to catch up with Lightning when he nearly spun out on a left turn.

"How do you make those left turns so well?" Francesco asked Lightning.

"Get equipped with some treaded tires," said Lightning. "Then turn right to go left. A very good friend taught me that once."

They finally stopped to rest.

Francesco sighed. "Ahh, Italia is beautiful, no? Just like Francesco!"

Lightning chuckled. "Do you always think about yourself?" he asked.

"Of course," said Francesco. "On the racetrack, Francesco only thinks about himself and doing his best. This is why he always wins!"

The next day was the big race. Finally, the world would find out who was the fastest race car! When the flag dropped, the fans went wild!

Francesco came out of the first left turn ahead of Lightning. He showed off his new treaded tires. "Perhaps Lightning has taught Francesco too well!" Lightning couldn't help but smile.

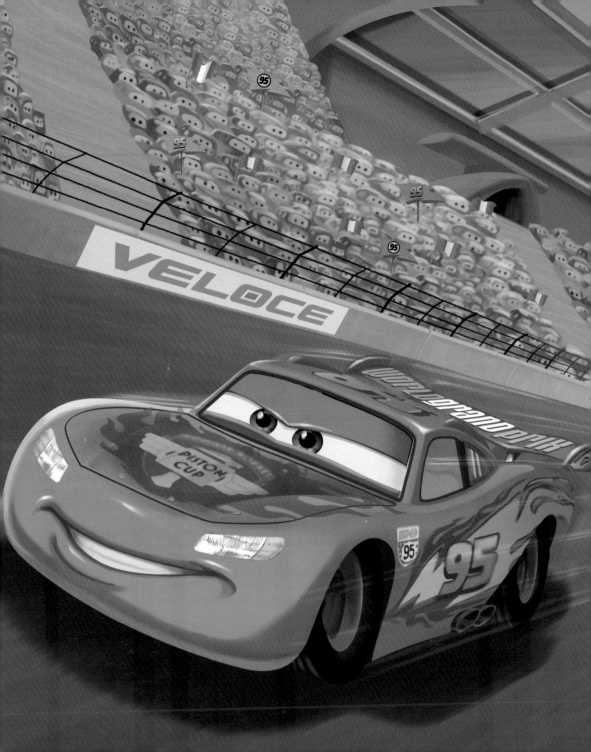

The racers entered the Monza arena and made a pit stop. As Lightning zoomed out of the pits, he got distracted by the camera flashes and the screaming fans. Suddenly Lightning remembered what Francesco had said about focusing on himself and doing his best. Lightning looked straight ahead and took the lead!

CAR BONARA

As the two cars crossed the finish line, the crowd gasped.

"Ka-chow!" yelled Lightning. "I won!"

"You mean ciao bella," said Francesco. "Francesco won!"

The truth stunned everyone. According to the judges, the race was a ... TIE!!!

The cars tried to figure out what to do.

Then Francesco shouted, "No more talk! Talk is slow. What do we do? We race!"

"That's a great idea!" said Lightning. "We'll race in Radiator Springs!"
Then the two fastest cars in the world zoomed away
together ... to race again another day.

The End

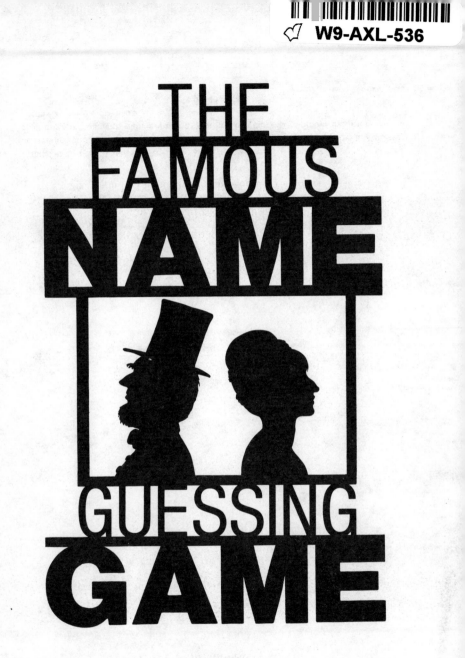

THE FAMOUS NAME GUESSING GAME

BY BILL BARR

Published by Price Stern Sloan Publishers, Inc.
360 North La Cienega Blvd., Los Angeles, California 90048

ISBN 0-8431-2306-0

*For my son Adam, who asked
the most important question,
"Where's the money?"*

Introduction

*Play them with friends
or enjoy them by yourself!*

Each page contains a fun, fact-filled biography of a famous person. The identity of the subject is gradually revealed as you proceed from one fascinating clue to the next!

Directions for Group Play

1. One player reads the clues, pausing after each to give the group a chance to guess the identity of the subject.

2. When a player guesses the identity of the subject, he or she is awarded the points shown to the right of the last clue read. (The answers to each game are found on the following pages.)

3. A different player becomes the reader for each new subject, giving all a chance to participate.

4. A game consists of any agreed upon number of subjects.

A Comic Genius

Points

He was born in London in 1889 .... **10**

He died in 1977 .... **9**

He was an actor, director, producer,
writer and composer **8**

He became famous playing a
pathetic underdog **7**

He became a professional performer
at age eight **6**

He was discovered by Mack Sennett,
who cast him in his first film **5**

He went on to make twelve feature films **4**

His now-famous costume consisted of
baggy pants, bowler hat, cane and
scraggly moustache **3**

He married Oona O'Neill and one
of their daughters is Geraldine **2**

His movies include "The Tramp,"
"Shoulder Arms," "The Kid" and
"The Gold Rush" **1**

Charlie Chaplin

A Sexpot of the Past

Points

She was born in Los Angeles in 1926 .... **10**

She grew up to become one of the world's most-discussed women **9**

During World War II, she worked in a defense plant **8**

She modeled for army pin-ups **7**

She bleached and shortened her hair to further her modeling career **6**

In the 1940s, she was paid $50 to pose for a nude calendar photo **5**

She was married to Joe DiMaggio and Arthur Miller **4**

It is rumored she was close friends with both John and Bobby Kennedy **3**

She starred in such films as "The Seven Year Itch" and "Some Like It Hot" **2**

She died in 1962 under mysterious circumstances **1**

Marilyn Monroe

She Sees Red

Points

She was born in Jamestown, New York in 1911 .... **10**

At age nineteen she was a platinum blonde named Diane Belmont **9**

She modeled and played bit parts in Broadway musicals **8**

She began her film career as a Goldwyn girl in "Roman Scandals" **7**

She gradually established herself as a female clown, and frequently co-starred with Bob Hope and Red Skelton **6**

She married a bandleader with an accent **5**

In the 1950s, she and her husband began one of the most successful comedy shows in TV history **4**

Before they were divorced in 1960, they had one of the world's most successful TV companies **3**

The Cuban bandleader was Desi Arnaz **2**

That show, of course, was "I Love Lucy" **1**

Lucille Ball

Mr. Macho

Points

He was born in Georgia in 1936 .... **10**

He is the grandson of a Cherokee
Indian **9**

He won a college football scholarship
but had to quit because of a knee
injury **8**

In New York City, he bounced drunks
and washed dishes to pay the rent **7**

He appeared in the TV series
"Riverboat" and "Gunsmoke" **6**

He became a movie stunt man and
gained fame on TV talk shows **5**

He was married to Judy Carne of
"Laugh-In" fame **4**

He has had long relationships with
Dinah Shore, Sally Field and
Loni Anderson **3**

He starred in "The Longest Yard,"
"Semi-Tough," "Smokey and the Bandit"
and "Hooper" **2**

He was the first nude male
centerfold in "Cosmopolitan"
magazine **1**

Burt Reynolds

Her Future is High and Mighty

Points

"People" magazine estimated her
public relations value to her
country at about $500,000,000 .... **10**

Her husband might dispute that **9**

She was born in Europe to a titled
family in 1961 .... **8**

She attended a Swiss finishing
school **7**

She was introduced to a young man
with royal connections **6**

They became engaged in 1980 .... **5**

A year later they were married in
what has been termed, "the wedding of
the century" **4**

The wedding was witnessed by a TV
audience of 750 million **3**

She may one day become queen of
England **2**

Her husband is Charles, Prince of
Wales **1**

Princess Diana

Who's the Boss?

Points

He was born in Illinois in 1911 with
the middle name Wilson **10**

He played football in high school
and college **9**

He announced Chicago Cubs football
games on the radio **8**

He became a movie actor and made
"Knute Rockne - All American" **7**

On TV, he hosted the G.E. Theater **6**

He was once president of the Screen
Actor's Guild **5**

His nickname is "Dutch" **4**

His first wife was Jane Wyman **3**

He was twice elected governor of
California **2**

In 1980 and 1984, he was elected
president of the U. S. **1**

Ronald Reagan

Part of
an Acting Family

Points

She was born in New York City in 1937 .... **10**

Her father was a famous actor and
her mother a socialite **9**

She didn't consider an acting career
until she appeared in "The Country
Girl" with her father **8**

She studied art in Paris and modeled
in Manhattan **7**

Her face appeared twice on the cover
of "Vogue" magazine **6**

She played a space maiden in
"Barbarella," which was directed by
her first husband, Roger Vadim **5**

She starred in "Barefoot in the
Park," "Julia," "The Turning Point,"
"Klute" and "Coming Home" **4**

She co-starred with her father,
Henry, in "On Golden Pond" **3**

She won an Emmy for "The Dollmaker"
and starred in "Agnes of God" **2**

Millions have tried her "workout" on
video cassette **1**

Jane Fonda

Politics and Poker

Points

He was born in the Middle West in 1884 .... **10**

He was rejected by West Point for
bad eyesight, but became an
infantry captain in World War I **9**

He married Miss Wallace and they
called their daughter "Baby" **8**

He bacame a Jackson County judge,
and later was elected to the U.S. Senate **7**

With his partner, Eddie Jacobson, he
opened a haberdashery that failed **6**

In 1944, he was elected
vice-president when FDR ran for a
third term **5**

His wife was Bess and his daughter
is Margaret **4**

He had a sign on his desk that read,
"The buck stops here." **3**

He was noted for playing "The
Missouri Waltz" on the piano **2**

When Roosevelt died in 1945, this
man from Independence, Missouri
became President **1**

Harry S. Truman

A
One-time
Vaudevillian

Points

She sang, danced and acted through thirty-four films in twenty-seven years **10**

She was born in Minnesota in 1922 .... **9**

Her family was in vaudeville, and by age five she was an old pro **8**

George Jessel suggested she change her family name, Gumm **7**

In 1938, she sang "Dear Mr. Gable" to Clark's picture **6**

She was married a total of five times **5**

One marriage was to Vincent Minnelli **4**

Her daughters are Liza and Lorna **3**

She co-starred in nine films with Mickey Rooney **2**

She played Dorothy in "The Wizard of Oz" **1**

Judy Garland

A Late Bloomer

Points

Her real last name is Driver **10**

She was born in Ohio in 1937 .... **9**

Thirty-seven years later she made
her debut as a comedienne **8**

In her first act, she emphasized her
ability as a piano virtuoso and
impersonator **7**

She was so good she lengthened her
first engagement from fourteen days
to eighty-nine weeks **6**

She went from San Francisco's Purple
Onion to national success **5**

She portrayed a frowzy,
self-mocking, mop-headed housewife
with a raucous laugh **4**

Her image has improved through
face-lifts and an upbeat wardrobe **3**

She made her first husband
nationally famous **2**

She called her first husband "Fang" **1**

Phyllis Diller

Mr. Success

He was born in Brooklyn in 1961 .... **10**

His fame has spread through TV, film
and records **9**

Like many kids, he spent long hours
in front of the TV **8**

He specialized in imitating
Bugs Bunny and Laurel and Hardy **7**

Shortly after high school, he became
a regular on an NBC-TV show **6**

He became an overnight sensation
doing his classic impression of
Little Richard **5**

Some of his fellow laugh-getters
were Joe Piscopo and Martin Short **4**

After he left "Saturday Night Live,"
he made his film debut in "48 Hours" **3**

He starred in such blockbusters as
"Trading Places" and "Beverly Hills
Cop I and II" **2**

His hit record is "Party All the
Time" **1**

Eddie Murphy

A Smart Dummy

She was born in San Francisco in 1906 .... **10**

Her three middle names were Ethel,
Cecile and Rosalie **9**

She was convent-educated until age
fourteen **8**

She joined her sisters' vaudeville
act and met a young comic **7**

When she became Mrs. Birnbaum, she
and a young comic formed a lifelong
partnership **6**

Before she retired, she and her
husband starred on stage, screen,
radio and TV **5**

She died in 1964, but her husband is
still busy at age ninety-one **4**

Her husband smokes cigars and jokes
about chasing young girls **3**

She and her husband, George, closed
each show when he said "Say
goodnight, Gracie" **2**

Naturally, she said "Goodnight,
Gracie" **1**

Gracie Allen

A Track Star

Points

His hobby is driving a race car **10**

He was born in Ohio in 1925 with
the middle name Leonard **9**

He drives a Nissan 300 ZX, in which
he has won several races **8**

Before he began racing in 1972,
he spent many years concentrating
on his acting career **7**

He made his Broadway debut in
"Picnic" **6**

He attracted attention in the film
"Somebody Up There Likes Me" **5**

He usually portrays outsiders or
rebels **4**

His movies include "Cat on a Hot
Tin Roof," "The Hustler," "Hud"
and "Cool Hand Luke" **3**

He won an Oscar for "The Color of
Money," after six prior nominations **2**

His wife is Joanne Woodward **1**

Paul Newman

A Busy Body

He was born in the South in 1935
with the middle name Aron **10**

He had a twin brother who died at birth **9**

His deeply religious father insisted
he sing in church **8**

He got his first guitar at age
twelve, and by the mid-1960s, he was
the highest-paid performer in history **7**

Before he began his phenomenally
successful singing career, he was an
usher and truck driver **6**

He learned hillbilly and blues songs
from records **5**

He made his first commercial record
in 1954 under the guidance of his
manager, a man named Parker **4**

He caused a sensation on "The Ed Sullivan
Show," although viewers couldn't see his
frenetic pelvic movements **3**

He died at his Memphis home,
"Graceland," in 1977 .... **2**

His smash hits include "Heartbreak Hotel,"
"Hound Dog" and "Blue Suede Shoes" **1**

Elvis Presley

A Famous Founding Female

Points

She was born in Virginia in 1731 .... **10**

Her father was a wealthy landowner **9**

Her maiden name was Dandridge **8**

She married a rich man who left her
a wealthy widow **7**

Her second husband was somewhat
younger than she **6**

Her husband served in the
Continental militia **5**

She shared hard winters with her
husband in New Jersey and at Valley
Forge **4**

She dressed so plainly many people
thought she was the family maid **3**

Her husband called her by her
childhood nickname, "Patsy" **2**

When her husband was inaugurated
president in 1789, she became the
first first lady of the U.S. **1**

Martha Washington

A Hollywood Nice Guy

Points

He was born in Philadelphia in 1908 .... **10**

He was given the middle name
Maitland **9**

His family ran a hardware store **8**

He was a boy magician and
accordianist **7**

He attended Princeton University,
where he roomed with Henry Fonda **6**

They were both active in the
Triangle Club, which was devoted to
acting **5**

He served in the air force in World
War II, and became a general **4**

He starred in "Harvey," both on
Broadway and the big screen **3**

His movies include such hits as "You
Can't Take It With You" and "No Time
for Comedy" **2**

He won an Oscar for "Mr. Smith Goes
to Washington" and "Philadelphia
Story," with Katharine Hepburn **1**

Jimmy Stewart

A Conversationalist

Points

She was born in Brooklyn about
1935 .... **10**

Her family name was Molinsky **9**

As a child, she was so fat she was
her own buddy at camp **8**

She embarked on a show biz career
in 1960 .... **7**

She gave her male hairdresser a
feminine name **6**

She wrote for "Candid Camera,"
Phyllis Diller and Bob Newhart **5**

In 1965, she married Edgar and was
on the "Tonight" show for the
first time **4**

She was often a guest host on the
"Tonight" show, and for a time was
Carson's sole replacement nine
weeks a year **3**

She left that show in 1987 to host
her own late night show **2**

Her show failed and she is now a
star on "Hollywood Squares" **1**

Joan Rivers

A Legend in His Own Time

Points

He was born in England in 1903 .... **10**

His family moved to Cleveland, Ohio **9**

He won a boyhood contest imitating
Charlie Chaplin **8**

He became a boxer, but gave up the
ring in favor of a career as a
song-and-dance man **7**

His first major Broadway role was in
"Roberta" **6**

During the 1930s, he began a career
on radio and in films **5**

He has frequently emceed the Academy
Awards **4**

During World War II, he often
entertained U.S. troops overseas **3**

He made seven "Road" pictures with
Bing Crosby **2**

His evergreen theme song is "Thanks
for the Memories" **1**

Bob Hope

A Major
Crowd-Pleaser

Points

He was born in Chicago in 1901 and
moved to Kansas City, Missouri **10**

He grew up to become one of the most
famous names in show biz history **9**

He began as an artist **8**

He became a film producer and an
entrepreneur **7**

Over a period of fifty-six years,
his films won forty-eight Oscars
and seven Emmys **6**

His first series of animated cartoons
was titled "Oswald the Rabbit" **5**

He made "Steamboat Willie," which
featured a mouse **4**

Later he made "Three Little Pigs,"
"Pinnochio," "Fantasia" and
"Mary Poppins" **3**

Famous amusement parks in Florida
and California bear his name **2**

But it all goes back to the little
guy who started it all—Mickey Mouse **1**

Walt Disney

A Shooting Star

Points

Her estimated income will total
about forty-seven million dollars
for the past two years **10**

She was born in Michigan in 1959 .... **9**

She grew up to become a singer **8**

Her first album sold nearly three
million copies **7**

She has been known for a risque
belt buckle and fluorescent
rubber bracelets **6**

Her second album, "Like a Virgin,"
sold 4.5 million copies **5**

Her female fans were once called
"wanna-bes" **4**

Her "Material Girl" and "Papa
Don't Preach" were major hits **3**

She starred in "Desperately
Seeking Susan" **2**

She has a rocky marriage to
Sean Penn **1**

Madonna

A Tail Wagger

Points

He was born in Chicago in 1926 .... **10**

His parents forbade drinking,
smoking and swearing **9**

Sex was never mentioned in his house **8**

In 1953, he launched a new
publication **7**

The first issue of his publication
carried a nude photo of Marilyn Monroe **6**

The circulation of his publication
eventually grew to five million **5**

The 7-11 stores no longer carry his
magazine **4**

He had a large chain of
restaurant-nightclubs
bearing the name of his magazine **3**

He named the skimpily clad
waitresses "bunnies" **2**

He publishes "Playboy" **1**

Hugh Hefner

A Hillbilly Star

She was born in Tennessee in 1948
with the middle name Rebecca **10**

Her family was so poor she had to
use Mercurochrome for make-up **9**

She sang gospel music in the church
where her grandfather preached **8**

She played snare drums in her high
school band **7**

She has been named best female
vocalist and best female songwriter **6**

She wears low-cut outfits that
accentuate her positives **5**

She wears huge, curly blonde wigs
and lots of make-up **4**

She starred in the films "9 to 5"
and "Best Little Whorehouse in
Texas" **3**

She operates an amusement park
called "Dollyland" **2**

Her weekly ABC-TV show was
cancelled in 1988 .... **1**

Dolly Parton